Living Well By Water

Stan Moore

First Printing 2001

ISBN 0-9706014-1-7

Words of Life Fellowship Church
20051 NE 15th Court
North Miami Beach, FL 33179

Contents

Foreword

In 1977, I first met Stan Moore when I was preaching at a Christian retreat in Bradenton, Florida. The Lord used my testimony and teaching on the power of the Blood to influence an awesome miracle for Stan's son at their home in Miami.

We didn't meet again until October 2000, when he and his wife Geri were ministering at Victoria, British Columbia, in Canada. My wife Debra and I attended their meetings where Stan shared powerful truths and facts about the importance of water. His scriptural and practical presentations impacted us deeply. We left those meetings persuaded in our hearts we would respond to this sound but almost revolutionary teaching. The results have been very positive. Both Debra and I have committed ourselves to drinking large quantities of pure alkaline water. This action has greatly improved our health and has been beneficial to many others with whom we have endeavored to share this delightful "water practice."

In his new book, Pastor Stan Moore unfolds principles of life and Scripture that are very motivational. I know many testimonies have poured into Pastor Stan's ministry about the benefit of his water teaching. On May 31, 2001, my wife and I were guests in his truly great church in North Miami Beach, Florida. It was obvious Pastor Stan's ministry has resulted in establishing a church excited about the Word and the Spirit. I know as you read this book with an open heart and mind, then begin to drink water like you never have before, your life will be blessed abundantly.

—Don Gossett

"Finally, brethren, whatever things are true, whatever things are noble, whatever things are just, whatever things are pure, whatever things are lovely, whatever things are of good report, if there is any virtue and if there is anything praiseworthy—meditate on these things."

—Philippians 4:8 (*NKJV*)

Preface

This book by any standard might seem to be a very unusual one coming from the desk of a pastor. But then, in some respects, it might take a pastor's heart to pursue such a topic, given the fact that a true pastor only wants the best—total well-being—for the sheepfold. But most of all, I want to convey to you how important water is to your health by showing you the reality of how God Himself used water. He gave us the parallel of water and its benefits for spiritual enlightenment and life and, literally, for physical healing.

Introduction

Teaching about water does not seem very spiritual, but in this book I am going to show you that natural water can be spiritual in that God uses water to bless His people.

When the Lord laid this message on my heart, I said, "Are You sure You want me to teach on this? This is something that might be controversial. It might be something that people will come against." You see, I'd never heard anyone in the Church teach on what I was learning about water, so I debated whether I should take this to my congregation. But the Lord said to do it, so I did it.

When I first stepped out and began teaching on water, the devil put this thought in my head, "The people are not going to receive this, because it's too much of a change. It is too big a departure from what they have been hearing and doing."

But as you read, you will see that though drinking natural water for health, wholeness, and soundness for your body may sound different from what you have heard before, it is not a departure from healing at all. It is only another aspect of the subject of healing. It is another side of the mountain—another vantage point—but it is the same mountain of healing.

As I began to teach on water in relation to healing and health, I did meet with some resistance. You can always tell when there is resistance. People get tense when they have to change their habits. I agree that we should not change good habits; however, we should do what is required to change bad habits to help and better ourselves.

I began to teach my congregation, explaining, in short, that although we may be spiritually drinking from the water of the Word, there is a natural part that we must attend to also.

Later on, I ministered at a pastors' convention where at least one hundred pastors were in attendance. I asked how many of them drank at least eight glasses of water per day. To my surprise, not many hands went up. So I asked, "How many of you drink *seven* glasses of water a day?" A few responded. I kept reducing the number, until I discovered that the average number was *two glasses of water per day*! And that was only among the few who responded. Many of the pastors drank more soda than water!

I pulled out a dry, brittle kitchen sponge and passed it around. I asked each one to feel it and then pass it to the next person without saying anything. After everyone had a chance to handle the sponge, I said, "That is what your insides are like when you're dehydrated." Well, they looked at me kind of odd, as if to say, *How spiritual is this?*

I went on and taught those pastors some of the information contained in the following pages of this book. Afterward, a number of them said to me, "God has been dealing with me for several years about drinking water. Your message convicted me. It is 'right on'!"

You see, what I taught them bore witness with their spirits. One way to keep from getting off base is to submit your revelation to your peers in ministry. They can help judge the accuracy of your revelation.

Since the time of that meeting, God has increased my knowledge of water's healing power. I believe the information contained in the following pages will bless you tremendously as it has blessed me, my family, and others to whom I have ministered the message.

Chapter 1

One Word Can Change Your Life

Let me explain how this book actually came about. In December 1999, I sought the Lord concerning the direction for the year 2000 and the new millennium.

After much prayer, I sensed that the foundational scripture for our people was to be Third John 2: *"Beloved, I wish above all things that thou mayest prosper and be in health, even as thy soul prospereth."* But I was strongly impressed that we were to focus more on "be in health."

Any born-again child of God who has studied the Scriptures knows that God is a loving heavenly Father and that He wants us well. He wants us healthy and strong in every area of our lives. Jeremiah 30:17 says, *"For I will restore health unto thee, and I will heal thee of thy wounds, saith the Lord...."*

God wants you to be spiritually strong in faith, in the Word, in redemption, in righteousness, and in the love of the Father. He wants you to be well in mind—mentally and emotionally. He wants you to have a healthy will—one that always aligns with His will.

According to Third John 2, your heavenly Father wants above all things that your body be well. He wants you free from the bondages of sickness, disease, and illness. He wants you free from pain, from depression, from the worries and woes of this earthly life. Our heavenly Father wants us healed. Psalm 107:20 says, *"He sent his word, and healed them, and delivered them from their destructions."*

In obedience to the instructions and direction I was given, I began to teach on all the ways that Jesus has provided for us to be healed. It took me six months to cover all the ways that God has shown us in His holy written Word.

One of the foundational scriptures on healing is First Peter 2:24, which says, *"...by whose stripes ye were healed."* Through this scripture, Jesus is essentially saying, "By My stripes you are healed." Jesus wants us healed and well. So, *legally*, healing and wellness are ours. But are we *vitally* experiencing healing and wellness?

Have We Missed Something?

As I studied and meditated and taught about all the ways that Jesus has available to heal us, I was amazed that anybody could be sick! One night I said to the Lord, "Lord, I know You want us healed from whatever infirmity that would strike us. Yet the more I teach, the more I am convinced You don't want us to even get sick so that we need Your healing grace."

I continued, "I am a father, and if my boys are sick, I want them well. But as a father, I don't want them sick in the first place. So as my heavenly Father, You must not want us sick at all, either. Father, I believe we have missed or unconsciously overlooked something that is probably as plain as the nose on our face. I believe that it is so simple and inexpensive that it is available to the entire world."

I did not force the issue in my studies, but I meditated more and more on the fact that our Father God does not want us sick.

I know that the world's system is designed to communicate to us all the reasons we are sick. It attributes sickness and disease to poor diet, stress, lack of exercise, lack of vitamins—and the list goes on. One popular magazine even printed an entire issue dedicated to the subject of health, entitled, "1,001 Ways To Stay Healthy." But I needed *God's* answer on this issue.

One Word From God

Early one morning, about 4:00 a.m., one word came to me: water. I knew that one word from God could change our lives. The word water would not leave me, so I began to find in the Scriptures what my Father God says about water.

I knew that in the spiritual respect water was, is, and always will be a vital portion of our lives, but I was not prepared for the scriptural discussion of the *natural* benefits of water. I found that there are more than 700 scriptures dealing with water, both spiritually and physically, from Genesis to Revelation. (For a partial listing of these scriptures, please *see* Appendix B.)

I began to focus on the multitude of ways that water benefits our bodies and the absolute necessity of water in our lives. Basically, we can do very little without water in the natural sense, from the time we get up until we go to bed.

We Need Water

Water is a part of our everyday lives. We drink it, cook with it, clean with it, and bathe or shower with it. Water is necessary for every function of life.

Have you ever worked hard and became dirty and sweaty? When you feel like that, do you just go right to bed? No, you're so thirsty, you gulp down a glass of water and say, "That's good!" After that, you probably step into the shower, and when you do, the minute that water washes over you, you think, *That feels good!* But what if you didn't have enough water to take a shower for a couple of weeks? You would be miserable. And if you didn't have enough water to drink, you would eventually die.

Even our automobiles run on water. If you removed the water from your car, you would have a big problem. Sometimes people have car trouble because their cars run out of water. Maybe they have failed to check the water level. The next thing they know, their cars are barely cranking along, and smoke is coming out of their hoods, or their cars stop completely because the engines are worn out.

On a larger scale, some of the biggest energy plants in the world are hydroelectric; they use water to provide electricity. Our oceans and waterways also provide important avenues of transportation that support our system of commerce. Some of the largest cities in the world are generally built on or near the water. For example, Miami, Florida, is surrounded by water. We need water!

God gave us water so we could live. He gave it to supply a need, and He also gave it for our enjoyment. My family goes on cruises; and for recreation, we also like to ride speedboats in the ocean waters near where we live. We are especially thankful for all the water God put on the earth!

A Priceless Resource

Everyone uses this valuable commodity, yet we don't usually think of water as valuable. We think of crude oil and natural gas that we use for fuel and heat as valuable. But we've taken the priceless resource of water for granted.

In 1992 south Florida was devastated by hurricane Andrew, which caused one of the worst natural disasters in the United States. More than 185,000 homes were destroyed. The one commodity that was the most essential in that tragedy was water. Greedy people were selling water at a premium. You see, when you have no water, it becomes extremely valuable.

Don't Dry Up

Spiritually speaking, without the Word of God, everything dries up. So naturally speaking, without water, everything dries up as well.

Make a note of this phrase "dries up," as it is about to become important in your life. "Dries up" means *dehydrated*. Take note of that; your knowledge of that word is going to play a vital part in your life.

As I studied this topic at the Lord's direction, I thought back to the years when I played football in high school and college. One thing that coaches required of us was to drink plenty of water and take salt pills, if needed, so we did not become dehydrated. They knew that if we "dried up," our energy levels would decrease, and we could not perform at our maximum efficiencies.

I also thought back to my Army times during World War II. Our instructors would tell us that there were three things we had to protect—our lives, our guns, and our *canteens*! Why our canteens? We could exist up to forty days without food, but only about seven days without water. Our instructors also said, "A man who is desperate for water will do anything to get your canteen."

I remembered from health class that it is important to drink from eight to ten glasses of water per day for maximum health. As I studied the Scriptures and began to search out everything I could about water from the medical and scientific fields, the word water became very prominent in my thinking.

Divine Health in a Five-Letter Word?

When God created this planet, He made it approximately 75 percent water and 25 percent land. Similarly, when God created man, He made him approximately 75 percent water and 25 percent substance.

In my research through the medical journals, I found that the brain, the eyes, the ears, the vital organs, the skeletal system, the cells, the immune system, tissues, and so forth, are approximately 75 to 85 percent water. The brain alone is approximately 85 percent water. The amazing fact is that the blood is approximately 90 to 94 percent water.

We really can't live well without sufficient water. The blood, the brain, and the entire body absolutely depend on water. Leviticus 17:11 says, *"For the life* [vital portion] *of the flesh is in the blood...."*

God's one word was beginning to make much more sense to me now. I started to ask myself, *Can divine health be as simple as a five-letter word, w-a-t-e-r?*

Chapter 2

If You're Not Thinking Water, You're Not Thinking Health And Longevity

I began to see that water is one of the main building blocks of all creation. I found that water is second only to oxygen as essential for life. As a matter of fact, water is H_2O: two parts hydrogen, one part oxygen.

The more I searched, the more the Holy Spirit began to give me revelation knowledge and understanding of the importance of water for our well-being. He showed me that we truly can live well by water. This is not abstract theory — it is an absolute!

I began to collect facts about water, including the following golden nuggets of truth:

• Water is the cash flow to the body.

• Water shortage can lead to the bankruptcy of our health.

• Water is more important to life's essential processes than any other substance we know.

• Water sustains all forms of life on the earth, including human life.

• Water is a vital compound that the body needed, does need, and will need at all times, and in sufficient quantity.

• Water is the vital solvent of the body that regulates all of the vital functions of our bodies from the top of our heads to the bottom of our feet.

• Water must be available to carry vital elements—oxygen, hormones, and chemical messengers to all parts of the body.

• Water is also needed in the very important process of carrying toxic waste away from the cells. In fact, there are at least fifty reasons why the body needs sufficient water on a regular basis.

• Water is absolutely vital for health and longevity in God's plan for His people. *If you are not thinking water, you are not thinking health and longevity.*

• Water is the greatest health discovery of all times and a natural medication with supernatural implications for a variety of health conditions.

• Water is extremely valuable. Let there be a shortage of it, and this statement will prove itself true.

• Water, in the natural and spiritual, is God's power source for miracles.

If all of these nuggets are true, then why are so many people still sick? Why is it that we do not hear more about the importance of water from our healthcare professionals?

The Business of Medicine

The reason we haven't heard this message from our doctors may be that there is great profit in treating symptoms, but very little profit in getting people totally cured so that they walk in continual health. Medicine is a multi-trillion dollar business, yet basically all it does is treat symptoms. Why? Because if you're cured, you don't need to keep going back to the doctor or using medication. Thus, we have been operating on a *"sick*-care" system, not a *health*care system.

Now don't misunderstand me. I am not saying that all doctors treat only the symptoms with no concern for the root cause of the problem. And I am not saying that all doctors treat only the symptoms with the motive of keeping their patients dependent upon medical care for the doctors' and pharmaceutical companies' financial gain. I am simply saying that there is big money in treating symptoms. Treating symptoms is profitable to the medical field; our walking in health is not.

I don't know if you've noticed, but many drug companies are running television commercials and newspaper and magazine ads as never before. The propagation of prescription drugs, suggesting the management of diseases such as allergies, arthritis, and heartburn is widespread.

But all that advertising must be paying off. As I said, the drug businesses are multi-trillion dollar businesses. What I don't understand is why people would want to "manage" a disease and live on drugs when they can find a *cure* for the disease and live well—free from the potential side-effects caused by taking drugs.

Health Should Be Inexpensive and Easy

God wants us to be healthy and not to have to spend a lot of money doing it! That is why I don't think God would put us in a position of having to spend all of our money on doctors, medicine, or even health foods and nutritional supplements trying to be healthy.

Healing and health should not be an impossible or difficult goal. Healing and health are God's will, and He has made it easy to walk in them. Does

Third John 2 say, "Beloved, I wish above all things that you may prosper and be *sick as a dog*"? No! This verse says that God wants us to prosper and be in health!

The Well Has Run Dry

Why are we not enjoying the health that Jesus has provided for us? Because the well has run dry. Spiritually, we have become dry because we have not hungered and thirsted for the Word of God. Physically, we become dry because do not thirst for eight to ten glasses of water per day, but instead for all the substitutes on the market.

The human body gives many different indications when it runs short of water. When the body needs only water, it complicates matters if one gives the body artificial taste-enhancing fluids on a regular basis and in full substitution of the body's water requirements. This not only leads to chronic dehydration but brings the body's pH level into an overall acidic state. (Further discussion on pH levels will follow.)

As I studied and was learning all of these things, one thing was becoming obvious: As we get older and set in our ways, we can become completely oblivious to our need for water and lose the taste for it. Because of a gradually failing thirst sensation for water, our bodies become chronically and increasingly dehydrated from an early age on. The well runs dry (lacking or deficient in moisture). Portions of the functioning parts of the body dry up (more explicitly, they begin to disappear as if by evaporation, draining or cutting off a source of supply; they begin to to wither or die through gradual loss of vitality or life).

I knew I had found a major key to illness, sickness, and disease. It is dehydration.

Hydration Brings Vitality

Unfortunately, most of us have overlooked water as a method of healing or of preventing sickness. If I asked the average person if he believed that there is health in water, he would probably say yes. But if I asked how much water he drinks, he would probably say, "Well, I drink a lot of water." The truth is that most people do not drink more than a glass or two per day.

Your body needs water to function properly. When you put water into your body, your body soaks it up like a sponge and uses it to help keep "all systems go" and ensure a healthy physical makeup. But if you do not get adequate water, your body won't be able to function optimally, and you will notice it in ways you wouldn't ordinarily connect with a lack of this vital substance.

If we want to live healthy lives, our first thoughts should be on water. Instead, many of us have put our priorities of food, vitamins, exercise, and so forth. Water should come first, before these others, because these things only work efficiently and effectively with a proper quantity of water.

A body feels good when it is hydrated. A properly hydrated body becomes alive with energy, vitality, and strength.

Dehydration Brings *Dis*-Ease

Conversely, chronic dehydration produces many different diseases, illnesses, and pains in the body. When you deprive yourself of water, you are in the process of making yourself sick. Water activates your body's system to function properly, and the lack of it causes a variety of thirst responses, some of which we call sickness, disease, and pain.

Disease is *dis*-ease. It means the body is not at ease. An example of ease on the outside of the body is how the body responds to a nice warm shower or bath. You just feel good and clean: at ease. Con-

versely, disease makes the inside of your body feel
uncomfortable and painful: *dis*-eased.

Chronic dehydration damages the body and,
eventually, life itself. Remember, God has given
man a span of 120 years (Gen. 6:3). Why die early?

The Root Causes of All Major Diseases

In my opinion, chronic and persistently increas-
ing dehydration is one of the root causes of almost
all currently encountered major diseases of the
human body.

When doctors say they can't find the cause of
your feeling so bad, it is most likely at least partially due to dehydration. Sometimes it will cost
you thousands of dollars to find out that they can't
discover what is wrong with you, when it may simply be dehydration.

As I said, dehydration damages the body and,
eventually, human life itself. A dehydrated human
body can produce pain when it is thirsty. In a
national broadcast, it was announced that over 110
million Americans (Christians and non-Christians)
suffer from minor to chronic pain in various parts
of the body. Could dehydration be the reason for
those pains?

One of the primary causes of Alzheimer's disease is chronic dehydration of the brain cells. If there is a shortage of water in a pregnant mother's body, there is a shortage of water in the baby's body. This will cause damage to the baby.

Chronic cellular dehydration can painfully and prematurely kill. Its initial outward manifestations have until now been labeled as diseases.

Energize Your Body With Water

No matter what your age, begin to energize your body with the proper amount of water. The water of the Word energizes and enhances the spiritual man; likewise, water energizes and enhances the physical body.

Can we do something to be cured of pain and to prevent diseases? I believe we can. Galatians 3:13 says, *"Christ hath redeemed us from the curse of the law...."* Jesus reversed the curse. Thank God for His mercy and grace. It is vital to know that He loves us and wants us well.

When dehydration has become symptom-producing, Jesus has provided for the reversal of its complications. However, reversing the effects of chronic dehydration in order to walk in the health

He provided will take time, knowledge, understanding, and then action.

After taking the time to acquire knowledge on this topic, I discovered that the cure and prevention of diseases and illnesses in the natural sense is very simple: Begin to increase your water intake; move from a dehydrated state to a hydrated state.

At this stage of my study, I knew it was about time to begin teaching this topic at the Wednesday night Bible study at our church. I was determined to prove the validity of what I had learned.

Chapter 3
The Water Cure

Once, over a period of months, I periodically experienced severe heartburn. To relieve it, I took antacid medicine, which would temporarily cause the heartburn to subside. Yet it seemed to be getting worse, almost to the point that at times, I thought I was having a heart attack.

I decided I was going to put what I had learned about water to the test. I began to increase my water intake to the proper amount. However, for reasons I had yet to discover, I still wasn't getting the relief I had expected. Had I made a mistake? Had I missed God?

About this same time, I came across a book called *Reverse Aging* by a Korean scientist named Mr. Sang Whang of Miami, Florida. I tracked him down and met with him (to my surprise, he was an elder in the church where I had been born again and had myself been an elder). Thus, additional vital information came my way.

Not only do we have to be concerned about dehydration, I learned, but our overall pH reading must be largely alkaline. A pH reading determines whether a person's pH level is alkaline or acid. The pH reading in a person's body can range from 0 to 7 and from 7 to 14. A pH reading of 7.0 is neutral. Anything below 7.0 is acidic, and anything above 7.0 is alkaline. From that, I learned that God made the internal constitution of the body to be alkaline, which would be above 7.0.

Avoid Acidic Substitutes

Because we are designed to hydrate our bodies with water, we should not substitute water with soda, coffee, tea, or various other acidic fluids.

Since I didn't drink coffee or tea, I was down to soda. Then I discovered that most sodas are in the very low side of the 7.0 level, which is acidic.

The heartburn problem was getting worse, though I was drinking water. I liked soda, so I was between a rock and a hard place, so to speak. But I made a decision: The soda would have to go because I desired a healthy body more than I desired soda. I kept hydrating myself with water, and I quit the acidic soda "cold turkey."

Immediate Change

Immediately, a change took place in my body. The heartburn that had been so severe began to subside, and in a week, it disappeared. I was a happy camper!

To my surprise, I received other benefits from drinking the proper amount of water, which really made me happy. For years, I'd had very dry skin on my hands and arms. When I would scratch my arms, red "blood spots" would appear and remain for days. As I continued drinking water (alkaline) and stopped drinking soda (acidic), the dry skin began to disappear and there were no more blood spots.

Another benefit ensued, which pleased my wife. Previously, my energy level and vitality were running low. When we would come home from work at the church, we would sit down to read, study, or watch a good television program, I would fall asleep quickly. That lack of energy began to disappear because my body was beginning to come into the state in which God designed it to be. Know this: One thing that will make a wife happy is not sitting by herself all night!

God's Health Plan

Now I began to see that you can live well by water, and you can *stay* well by water. An ounce of prevention is worth a pound of cure!

Because I had proven that Father God's health plan is vital to a hurting world, I began teaching on the subject of living well by water. At that point, I knew that sickness and disease had two basic root causes: (1) *dehydration* and (2) *acidosis*.

I sought the Lord again about sharing this message, and although I didn't get a check in my spirit, or a "red light," I proceeded—howbeit with caution. I had a peace in my heart about sharing what I had learned.

Further Confirmation

About the time I thought I was ready to begin the teaching full force, I received further confirmation that this message was indeed from God. I came across a book entitled *Your Body's Many Cries for Water* by Dr. Fereydoom Batmanghelidj, an Iranian doctor who had spent two and a half years in an Iranian prison.

While awaiting his sentence to die, Dr. Batmanghelidj began helping prisoners who were sick.

Having no medicine, he used the only healing source he had available: water. In those two and a half years, he treated more than 3,000 prisoners with water, and they were all healed.

Later I met Dr. Batmanghelidj, and he said that God had given him this plan. I believe Dr. Batmanghelidj is one of the leading authorities in the world on water and its healing power.

Everything I had found out on my own was now being confirmed by his book. Two statements in particular that he made in his book will challenge your thinking:

(1) "You may not be sick, you just might be thirsty";

(2) "You do not treat dehydration with medications. You treat your thirst and dehydration with water."

I believe the Father God was confirming that He wants His people well—not just *healed* from illnesses or diseases, but *well*. God doesn't want us sick at all; He wants us to live well. I know as a father and pastor, I want that for my family and my congregation. Since *I* want that, how much more does the *Father God* want that?

God's Power Source

God provided a substance that would help ensure our freedom from sickness, disease, and pain: *water*. Water is God's power source for healing in the body. It doesn't matter how old you are, you do not have to live in pain. I believe you will see pain dissipate if you will do what is required. Whether it is sickness or pain, God has an answer that can deliver you from your distresses in your body and keep you free of pain and disease.

Let me also say that one of the requirements for longevity is a will to live. You must have the attitude, "Devil, you are not striking me out! As a matter of fact, I am going to hit a home run with the bases loaded!" God abhors death; He calls death an enemy (1 Cor. 15:26). He does not want you to die prematurely, so you must think as He does and have a fighting will to live.

Dr. Batmanghelidj's book contains many wonderful testimonies. I want to tell you about one in particular. It is the testimony of a woman who had such severe asthma attacks that the doctors told her she was not going to live. Her body was shutting down, and she was, in effect, preparing to die. The doctors had no medication to treat her severe asthma attacks. They said there was nothing they could do for her. If you have ever been told that, you know that is the time to jump up and say, "Maybe *you* can't do anything, but, praise God, I know who can—Jesus the Healer!"

One day the woman's pastor visited her in her home. He told her, "I am here because I have a word from the Lord for you."

"What is it?" she asked.

He said, "You are dehydrated, and that is why asthma is having a field day in your life. From now on, you are to drink at least eight to ten glasses of water a day."

She said, "I don't even like water."

"Nevertheless," her pastor said, "I am telling you what the Lord told me to tell you."

So she began to drink water. She would drink two glasses in the morning before she ate anything, two before lunch, two before dinner, and then a glass or two later.

She found that the more she drank water, the less she would have those attacks, which had been very frequent. After about nine months, she was totally cured of asthma!

A Covenant of Health

This woman was healed when she heeded the word of the Lord through one of His servants. The same can be true for every child of God who will listen to His instructions.

Exodus 15:26 says, *"...If thou wilt diligently hearken to the voice of the Lord thy God, and wilt do that which is right in his sight, and wilt give ear to his commandments, and keep all his statutes, I will put none of these diseases upon thee, which I have brought upon the Egyptians: for I AM THE LORD THAT HEALETH THEE."* This is God's covenant of health for His people.

In Exodus 23:25 God says, *"And ye shall serve the Lord your God, and he shall bless thy bread, and thy water; and I WILL TAKE SICKNESS AWAY FROM THE MIDST OF THEE."*

I believe that we children of God are to be the healthiest, happiest, and most joyful people on the face of the earth. We have a very large window of opportunity to believe God for our general health no matter how many healings we may have had over the years. If we obey Him, serve Him, pray, say, and do His Word, we have the best of two worlds. God can change our whole world spiritually, physically, financially, mentally, emotionally, and even socially.

God Wants to Add Life to Our Years

I had become thoroughly convinced that a lack of water was detrimental to our well-being. However, I needed to understand more about pH levels and how important they are for our overall health. I was in for a great awakening.

I began my research and found that God wants to add *years to our lives* and *life to our years*. One of the ways we can receive these blessings is to understand our bodies' pH levels.

What exactly is pH? It is the measure of the degree of acidity or alkalinity of a substance—in this case, the human body. The pH values range from 0-14. A pH of 0 to 6.9 is considered acidic; 7.0 is neutral, and 7.1 to 14 is considered alkaline. The proper pH level for the human body is between 7.0 and 7.35. A higher pH is too alkaline for the body.

Total healing or chronic illness only begins to take place when and if the blood is restored to a normal, slightly alkaline pH.

Our bodies' pH level affects everything about our health. Instead of asking others how they feel, we should be asking them, "What is your pH level?"!

Chapter 4
You Are What You Drink!

God has a way for you to get well that is so simple and so inexpensive. This is it: Drink more water! Cancer and other illnesses can thrive in an acidic body. They cannot thrive in an alkaline body. Acid is hot and fiery, but you can put out the fire by drinking more water!

The word acid means *sour and bitter*. Alkaline means *sweet*. In order to regulate your pH level so that it is alkaline (sweet), be sure to drink at least one-half of your body weight in ounces of water each day. Remember, water is the cash flow to the body.

The human body is made to naturally crave the appropriate amount of water. So if we're not drinking enough water, what are we drinking? I was about to find the answer.

A Casual Survey

As I began to deliver to my congregation the message on water and how it affects their health, they didn't fully grasp the magnitude of what was to come. I asked how many drank water. All hands went up. I asked how many knew that over the years they were to consume eight to ten glasses of water per day. Again, all hands went up.

Next I asked how many were drinking the required amount. *Fewer than five percent of the people raised their hands.*

Then I asked how many were drinking half that amount. About 15 percent more raised their hands. I realized that approximately 80 percent of my people were in trouble concerning their intake of water.

After more questioning, I found that 20 to 30 percent of our people thought they were doing well if they drank one glass of water per day! Then I discovered that some never drank any water at all in a day! Some hadn't had a full glass in months!

Well, if they were not drinking water, what were they drinking? The answer came very quickly: soda/cola, coffee, tea, juice, and so forth. Because there is some water in these substitutes, they believed they were consuming sufficient amounts of water.

Then I found out that 20 to 30 percent of my congregation were "sodaholics." Some would drink three liters or more per day. They were hooked.

But for many, it was unintentional; it was the result of a lack of knowledge.

A Report on Cola

It was at this point in my survey that I read a report I'd found to all of these soda drinkers.

"For those of you who love cola," I said, "just when you thought you knew everything..." Then I related the following facts:

- To clean a toilet, pour a can of cola into the toilet bowl. Let "the real thing" sit for one hour; then flush clean. The acid in the cola removes stains from vitreous china.

- To remove rust spots from chrome car bumpers, rub the bumper with a crumpled-up piece of aluminum foil dipped in cola.

- To clean corrosion from car battery terminals, pour a can of cola over them to bubble away the corrosion.

- To loosen a rusted bolt, apply a cloth soaked in cola to the bolt for several minutes.

- To remove grease from clothes, empty a can of cola into a load of greasy clothes, add detergent, and run through a regular cycle. The cola will help loosen grease stains.

• To clean road haze from your windshield, wipe with a cola-saturated cloth.

• To carry a certain cola syrup (the concentrate that mixes with soda to produce the soft drink), the commercial truck must use the "Hazardous Material" placard usually reserved for highly corrosive materials.

• The average pH balance of soda is 2.7 to 3.4. This acidity level is strong enough to dissolve teeth and bones! Someone put a broken tooth in a bottle of cola, and in ten days, it dissolved! Teeth and bones are the only human organs that stay intact for years after death. Imagine what the drink must be doing to your soft intestines and stomach lining!

• The human body stops building bones around the age of thirty. After that, it will dissolve about eight to eighteen percent of the bones each year through the urine. The amount it dissolves depends on the acidity of the food consumed (acidity does not depend on the taste of the food, but on the ratios of potassium/calcium/magnesium/etc. to phosphorus). All the dissolved calcium compounds accumulate in the arteries, veins, skin tissue, and organs. This affects the functioning of the kidney (kidney stones).

• Cola soft drinks have no nutritional value. They have a high sugar content, high acidity, and additives such as preservatives, colorings, and caffeine.

• Some people like to drink cold soft drinks after each meal. Guess what the impact is. The body has an optimum temperature of 37° Fahrenheit for the functioning of digestive enzymes. The temperature of cold soft drinks is much less than 37° Fahrenheit, sometimes quite close to 0. A cold drink lowers the effectiveness of digestive enzymes and puts stress on the digestive system; therefore, the body digests less food. The undigested food becomes fermented and produces bad-smelling gases. Then it decays and forms toxins, which are absorbed in the intestines, circulated in the blood, and delivered to the whole body. This spread of toxins can lead to the development of various diseases.

• Diet colas contain a sugar substitute called aspartame. Though aspartame is deadly, it is now in over 5,000 products. Usually, anything that says sugar-free has aspartame in it. Read your label for contents.

• Have you ever thought about what you drink when you drink an aerated drink (soda)? You gulp down carbon dioxide, something that nobody in the world would advise you to do. Some time ago, there was a competition at a certain university for who could drink the most sodas?" The winner drank eight large bottles and died on the spot because of too much carbon dioxide in the blood and not enough oxygen. From then on, the dean banned all soft drinks from the university canteen.

Destroyed for Lack of Knowledge

In Hosea 4:6, the Word of God says, *"My people are destroyed for lack of knowledge: because thou hast rejected knowledge, I will also reject thee, that thou shalt be no priest to me: seeing thou hast forgotten the law of thy God, I will also forget thy children."*

Remember this scripture. What we do and practice might become an open door for our children to walk through and do also.

The Rising Trend of 'Sodaholism'

In the last thirty to forty years, sodaholism has spread, like a forest fire, out of control. I know this is the true, because little by little, I was beginning to get hooked on cola myself. This addiction is overtaking many of us, and we don't even realize it.

One article I researched indicated that this nation now consumes more colas and soft drinks than pure water. In 1998 records indicated that 15 to 20 billion soft drinks were sold in the United States alone. This included cans and bottles of any size.

Through clever marketing and advertising campaigns, colas and soft drinks have become entrenched in our society in our lifetime. They have become readily accepted as harmless pleasures for children and adults alike.

Remember Hosea 4:6—a lack of knowledge can be fatal. There is nothing in soda that is of any value to our health. It might taste good, but damage is being done when we drink it.

We have got to make our stand for ourselves and our families, particularly our precious children, our gifts from God. Drinking soda has had a devastating effect on our lives and the lives of our children. Many of our young people are being eradicated through sickness. Why? I believe it is because they don't drink enough water, and they live on fast food and soda.

And I can tell you from all the research I've done, the older people get, the less they drink water. But when we get older, we need *more* water, not less. So we need to start drinking more water now. What a change this will make in the long-term health of a young person if he will start this good habit today.

No Compromise

I was so overwhelmed by the information I had collected about soda that I pulled all of it from our ministry. I've been told how much profit vending machines could generate for our church, but I will believe God for our finances and not compromise the health of our people and their children.

I visited some of our local food stores and measured the spaces allocated for water versus colas and soft drinks, beer, wines, and other assorted drinks which are all acidic. (Remember, acid is a destroying agent to our bodies over the long haul.) The acidic drinks took up about four times the floor space that water (alkaline) used.

The Church's Response

The first night I began teaching my congregation about the devastating effects of replacing water with other acidic drinks, I watched for a response. The room was very quiet and subdued.

Our people had never heard a teaching like this in a church service.

The next Wednesday service, though, the response was spectacular. I found out that a number of my people who had been sodaholics had been immediately set free. From then on, praise reports have been coming in.

One of the men in our church's ministry of helps had an immediate deliverance from colas. That second Wednesday service, he asked if he could give a praise report. He said he'd had a case of dandruff for years: It was all gone! He'd had severe low back problems — they were all gone!

Then we heard from his wife. Before the first Wednesday night teaching about water, she had basically drunk no water at all, but had thrived on soda. For years, she'd had a severe skin disorder on her face: The disorder was cured!

I put out a limited report of illnesses, diseases, and symptoms that thrive in a chronically dehydrated and acidic bodily environment. Many members of our congregation and my own family have received healing of many of the diseases in this list, which by no means is all-inclusive.

- Arthritic pain
- High blood pressure

- Back pain
- High cholesterol
- Diabetes
- Obesity
- Ulcers
- Asthma
- Migraine headaches
- Osteoporosis
- Allergies
- Learning disabilities
- Attention Deficit Disorder
- Hyperactivity
- Reflux
- Sinus pain
- Multiple Sclerosis
- Prostate and other cancers
- Impotence
- Heart disease
- Chronic Fatigue Syndrome
- Alzheimer's Disease
- Lupus
- Psoriasis

- Irritable Bowel Syndrome
- Skin disorders
- Paget's Disease
- Undiagnosed symptoms

By the second teaching on living well by water, we were off and running as a congregation—and we have not stopped yet!

Chapter 5
Your Body's Cries for Water

Do you have days, such as I have had, when your body is devoid of energy or vitality—days when you feel this way:

- tired
- stressed out
- flushed
- irritable
- anxious
- dejected
- depressed
- inadequate
- loaded down
- confused
- craving manufactured beverages

As we have seen, the human body gives many different indicators that it is running short of water. Drinking artificial taste-enhancing fluids as full substitution of the body's water requirement complicates matters.

Again, I am going to emphasize that acidosis and chronic dehydration have been devastating our bodies for years. They have been causing sickness, disease, illness, pain, and misery, none of which comes from a loving heavenly Father. Each is a result of the unwise choices we have made without knowledge.

One publication showed that increased consumption of soft drinks contributes to assorted adult diseases and conditions occurring in our teenagers and even younger children. Some conditions mentioned were osteoporosis, bone fractures, diabetes, and clogging of the arteries (atherosclerosis).

Thus, the long-term and constant use of soda, in particular as a substitute for water, should be presumed to be a major cause of many of the more serious health problems.

Cause of Death: Unknown

Not very long ago, I attended the homegoing service for a great man of God who had passed away. There I met a gracious lady whom I discovered to be the widow of a world-renowned pastor who had died several years before. Her husband was one of the leading ministers in the great Healing Revival of the 1940s and '50s.

After the memorial service, this woman asked me if we could just sit and talk a bit. Of course, I said yes.

As we talked, she began to unfold the story of how her husband's ministry grew over the years since the Healing Revival. Then she said, "You know, he should be alive today."

"What do you mean?" I asked.

She continued, "Well, my husband had never drunk cola or coffee. But about a year or two before he passed away, he began to regularly drink both cola and coffee."

I asked, "Well, what illness caused him to pass away?"

She answered, "The doctors don't know. They couldn't find the cause." I think she suspected that her husband's passing had something to do with his lifestyle changes in the previous year or two.

'I Hated Water!'

"Sodaholics" need to be set free from their addiction in the same way someone who's hooked on drugs or alcohol needs to be set free. One woman in my congregation told me, "Pastor, when you first started teaching us about water, I have to confess I hated the stuff. And I almost hated you for talking about it! That was because I realized that I was addicted, that I was a 'sodaholic.' But I received deliverance! Most of my adult life I have lived on nothing but soda. But that is all changed now, and I feel so much better."

This woman also related that she had been so consumed with her desire for soda that she would buy cases and cases of it when it was on sale. (I like a good sale as much as the next person. But even if a six-pack of name-brand soda dropped to 99 cents, I wouldn't buy it, because I know that drinking that soda will only do harm to my body.)

This woman related: "If I ever happened to run out of soda, I would run out and buy it no matter what it cost. I couldn't live without it. But now I drink water instead of soda. I am up to a gallon of water a day now, and I know that I am going to walk in complete health as God intended. Every time I take a drink of water, I think about how good it tastes and about what good it is doing to every cell in my body, because God designed the body to receive water in order to survive."

A Poor Substitute

Recently, when an office machine at our ministry needed repair, I met another man who would also discover the health benefits of water. When I walked into our office to meet this service representative, right off, I noticed a large bottle of diet soda on the table. (You see, the soda companies are not content to have people drink a little can of soda anymore. They want us to buy their twenty-ounce bottles, quarts, two-liter bottles, and so forth.)

I asked, "Whose soda is this?"

The young man from the company said, "It's mine, Pastor. I drink at least one of those every day."

I said, "What are you drinking that stuff for? Do you know what you are doing? You are slowly poisoning yourself by drinking that."

"Well," he said, "I was an alcoholic. When I got delivered from alcohol, I felt the need to pick something else to drink habitually, so I began drinking soda. I've actually been known to drink twelve cans of soda a day. But it took too much time to open all those cans, so I switched to the bigger bottles. I just go about my business drinking soda all day."

"How long have you been doing that?" I asked him.

"Twelve years," the man responded.

Then I asked, "Do you drink water?"

"No. I don't like the stuff," he said.

"Well," I said, "between the alcohol and the soda addictions, you are fortunate to be alive today. I am sure you've got some physical problems as a result of both."

The young man agreed: "Actually, I'm not in good shape. How did you know?"

It didn't take a genius to figure it out. Anyone who has been drinking that many sodas a day for twelve years has to have a health problem! I knew he was dehydrated and had acidosis.

I told him, "You know that alcohol is not good for you. But soda is not good for you, either, because it is acidic. It will turn the constitution of your body's fluids from alkaline to acid. And what does acid do? It burns, eats up, and destroys things it comes in contact with."

I went on to I tell this man, "Son, God has given you 120 years (Gen. 6:3), but you are going to die young if you don't change some things quickly."

I didn't say that to condemn this young man or to frighten him. I actually said it under the inspiration of the Holy Spirit. I believe it was intended to be a wake-up call, and I hoped the man would take me seriously.

Let me interject a thought here. We were not designed to pass away prematurely. God set a span of time for us—for mankind—to live. Genesis 6:3 says that He has given us 120 years. Now, if you don't believe that, then you are free to go home and be with the Lord at whatever age you decide you want to go. If you want to go at 70, that is your choice.

God has given us the right to make a choice, and I have decided that I am going to shoot for 120! The Lord wants us healthy so we can do all that He has for us to do. But if we contract a serious disease, our time could be cut short. God has too much for you and me to do for us to allow that to happen.

Now let me tell you the rest of the story about this young man. A few weeks after our conversation, I saw him again. He said, "Pastor, my wife wants to thank you and give you a big hug."

I said, "Why?"

"She wants to thank you because I am not a sodaholic anymore. I got delivered the day you spoke to me and prophesied over me."

Then he told me what happened. He related that for years, he had walked around with a migraine-type headache almost every day. He said that the pain had been so great that some days, he hadn't been able to see very well. He would take aspirin and whatever else he could, trying to get rid of the pain. But by taking over-the-counter drugs, which are mostly acidic, he had unknowingly been compounding the problem.

I said to the young man, "Is that it? I know you had more things bothering you than just migraine headaches."

He said, "You're right. I also had irritable bowel syndrome. I had chronic diarrhea, and I felt as if my insides were torn up. I kept going to the doctor, but he could never figure out exactly what was wrong."

Reader, let me ask you a question. Have you ever felt just terrible and gone to see a doctor, but he couldn't find what was wrong with you? Many times, doctors will say something like, "I don't know exactly what's wrong with you, but let's give you such-and-such kind of medicine and see if it helps."

But you do not change the acidic condition in your body or become "re-hydrated" with a drug prescription—only water can do that! Medication might relieve the symptoms, but what some medicines do over the long haul can be deadly. They can mask the real problem, and often the side-effects are worse than the symptoms.

Maybe you've been to several doctors, but no one has been able to give an accurate diagnosis. I believe the answer lies in drinking more water—probably a lot more water!

This man from the company went on to tell me, "I also had such backaches that my back felt like it was killing me at times." So he was taking medicine for the migraine headaches, medicine for the irritable bowel syndrome, and medicine for the back pain. He also told me that his heart had begun to bother him. This young man was practically a "walking dead man"!

He continued, "After I talked with you that day, I stopped drinking soda and started drinking water. And I want you to know that the migraines left, the diarrhea left, and the back pain is gone—every symptom I had has totally disappeared! But that is not the only reason why my wife wants to thank you. The real reason she wants to thank you is, I used to be irritable most of the time, and I harassed her almost constantly—but not anymore! I also suffered with depression, but now it is gone. My whole disposition has changed. I am now a joyful, happy man, and she has noticed it. That is why she wants to thank you."

Make the Adjustment a Priority

If you have not stopped drinking sodas yet, and you want to see an improvement in your health, you will have to make that adjustment a priority. Then you will have to follow through with it.

The devil would love it if we just ate and drank all the things that are acidic and never drank enough water, thus changing the natural makeup of the fluids in our bodies from alkaline to acid.

Now I am not saying you need to get in fear about having an occasional soda or cup of coffee. Just don't use them as a substitute for water. You don't have to "live" off those things.

I know of people who in the past drank sodas habitually but who now only have one occasionally, just here and there. Now they drink several extra glasses of water to cancel out the effects of all the acid they're consuming in just that occasional soda.

Alkaline Water Neutralizes Acid Wastes

The fact that alkaline neutralizes acid is a basic natural phenomenon. Alkaline water has no nutritional or medicinal value to cure disease. What it does is neutralize the acid wastes in the human body and liquefy them for elimination by the kidneys. In order to live long and healthy lives, we must rid our bodies of acidic waste.

When we understand the fact that adult degenerative diseases are caused by the accumulation of acidic waste, it is no mystery that drinking alkaline water will improve our health.

Acid coagulates blood. This makes it impossible for vital organs to receive enough oxygen. Thus, progressive and degenerative diseases are created.

Diseases do not spring up suddenly, as we assume. They are the result of long-term acidic buildup, even beginning at an early age. Alkaline water is the cleanest, simplest, least expensive, and most effective way to reduce acidic waste.

So in order to live long and healthy lives, we must rid our bodies of acidic waste. And we know now that the best and easiest way to do so is to liquefy the waste by neutralizing it with alkaline water. By eliminating acidic waste particles in the blood, we can avoid the risk of diseases that cause sudden death.

Water: The Cheapest Form of Medicine

Water is the cheapest form of medicine to a dehydrated body. As simply as dehydration will, in time, produce major diseases, well-regulated hydration will prevent them.

The proper intake of water will prevent diseases that affect the body and the mind. In fact, people with Alzheimer's Disease and children with learning disabilities should not drink anything other than water. Such individuals should definitely not consume any caffeine-containing beverages.

Every function inside the body is regulated by and dependent upon water. The brain, being approximately 85 percent water, must have water. The blood, being approximately 90 to 94 percent water, must have water.

Take Care of the One Body
God Gave You

From the information I have researched, I discovered that 75 to 80 percent of Americans are dehydrated, many chronically. Their pH readings are below 7.0, which indicates that they are acidic. But we can individually begin to turn those statistics around.

God gave each of us only one body. That should really make you think about what you are putting into your body. You should want to take care of it according to His design.

I want you to get hold of this. Christians need to know about this, because if anyone has a right to walk in divine health it is God's covenant people. God has so many ways for us to be healed that I am convinced He doesn't want us ever to be sick. So whatever we have to do to enjoy the blessings of healing and health, let's do it. And according to what I have discovered, it is as simple as drinking water.

Chapter 6
'Changing the Condition I Am In'

You may be wondering, *How can I change the condition I am in? Is there help for me?* Absolutely! For every situation or circumstance we are in, God's grace is sufficient. Why? Because He is a good God and because He loves us.

Believe it or not, He does not want you sick. He wants you well. Why? Because He loves you. John 10:10 says that the thief (the devil) is the one who comes to kill, steal, and destroy; but Jesus has come that we may have life and have it more abundantly. God wants us to live in the health He has provided through Christ. And as we have learned, walking in that divine health may even be as simple as a five-letter word: *w-a-t-e-r*.

An Easy 'Water Check'

You may wonder if you are consuming enough water. One easy way to check is to notice the color of your urine. The normal color of urine should not be dark. It should ideally be almost colorless to light yellow. If it begins to become dark yellow or even orange in color, you are becoming dehydrated. When urine becomes darker in color, it is very concentrated urine. It indicates that the kidneys are working hard to get rid of toxins in the body.

You can also check your pH level with litmus paper. (Because litmus paper was not readily available to many of the people in my church, those who had swimming pools checked their pH levels with their pool kits!)

Another Essential Ingredient: Salt

Another way to walk in health is to make sure you consume enough salt on a daily basis. Salt is an essential ingredient in the body. In their order of importance, oxygen, water, salt, and potassium rank as the primary elements for the survival of the human body.

Pliny, around 75 A.D., called salt "foremost among human remedies." He was right. You see, about 27 percent of the salt content of the body is stored in the bones in the form of crystals. It is said that salt crystals are naturally used to make bones hard. Salt will be taken out of the bones to maintain its normal vital levels in the blood. Thus, salt deficiency in the body could be partially responsible for the development of osteoporosis.

Low salt intake will contribute to a buildup of acidity in some cells. High acidity in the cells can damage the DNA structure and can be the initiating mechanism for cancer formation in some cells.

Here is a rule of thumb for daily salt intake: For every ten glasses of water, one should add about half a teaspoon of crystallized sea salt to the diet. I personally like to put it in the palm of my hand and lick it. Some prefer to put it in their water, shake it well and drink it. It has a sweet taste.

I would like to add that in my personal experience of drinking water and taking a pinch of crystallized sea salt every day, I have now stopped losing my hair. Praise the Lord! One way I can tell if I am not drinking the required amount is that when I comb my hair, I see strands of loose hair in my comb. Then I make sure I increase my water intake.

What Kind of Water?

With all the bottled water and water filters currently available, you may be wondering, *Do I need to drink a specific kind of water?*

In my opinion, ordinary tap water (unless there is proof of its being contaminated with chemicals and heavy metals, such as lead) is a good source of supply.

If there is a heavy taste or smell of chlorine in your tap water, do what many restaurants do: Place your water in an open container, leave it for a number of hours, then refrigerate it. It should then taste fine.

If you are concerned that your water source may be contaminated or impure, save yourself this anxiety. Install an effective carbon or charcoal filter on your kitchen faucet. I did this and checked my tap water at the water company and found it was alkaline, so I have had good results with it. My wife prefers a good, natural spring water. There are some out there, but check to make sure the pH level is alkaline, which is above 7.0.

Your body needs an absolute minimum of eight to ten eight-ounce glasses of water per day. Alcohol, coffee, tea, caffeine-containing beverages, and soda (diet or otherwise) don't count as water. The best time to drink water is before eating food—breakfast, lunch, and dinner—and two and one-half hours after each meal. Portion it out instead of trying to drink your daily requirement at one time.

Maintain Healthy Eating Habits

In addition to drinking plenty of water, we have to eat sensibly to maintain good health. I don't like to use the word "diet" because most diets are too difficult to maintain over an extended period of time. I am talking about eating sensibly as a lifestyle. In other words, pay attention to what you eat and endeavor to eat plenty of fruits and vegetables and lean proteins, such as chicken. Try to stay away from foods that have no nutritional value, and don't let fast food become a habit. Those kinds of foods won't do your body a bit of good, and, in fact, could harm you over time.

Number Two: We Need To Exercise

Along with water and healthy foods, our body needs exercise to stay healthy. Walking is the cheapest form of exercise in the world and, to me, the easiest. So I advise you to walk as much as you possibly can every day.

Some experts say that "4/40" is good to remember for basic walking for health. That means walking forty minutes, four times a week. But you don't have to walk forty minutes at a time, in one stretch, if you are not able to physically or if time doesn't permit it. You can break up your exercise

routine, striving for at least 160 minutes of walking each week, and still achieve the desired result
of better health.

Change Your Condition

In short, if you want to change the condition
you are in, this is what you should do. First, pray
and thank God for the good health that is about to
come your way. Then practice the following for
optimum health:

• Stop drinking soda as soon as possible. It is
acidic and detrimental to the body.

• Begin to drink alkaline water. Take your
weight, divide by two, and drink that amount of
water in ounces every day (approximately eight to
ten glasses of water per day).

• Divide the ounces or glasses so that you drink
a proportional amount of it about half an hour
before each meal. This helps the digestive system
function properly and get things working the way
God has designed them to function. Try not to
drink while you are eating.

• Take about one-half teaspoon of salt for every
eight to ten glasses of water. Crystallized sea salt
is good. If the doctor has told you not to use salt,
show him Dr. Batmanghelidj's book *Your Body's*

Many Cries for Water. Ask him to explain his reasoning in comparison to the author's reasoning. Water and salt keep the body in balance.

• Try to stay away from man-made or processed food as much as possible. Most are acidic.

• Eat more fruits and vegetables; they are water-soluble. Balance your meals with good common sense. Don't overindulge.

• Take natural vitamin and mineral supplements; they work well with sufficient water.

• Exercise: walk, swim, etc.

• Stay away from caffeine-containing substances. But if you do indulge in some of them, supplement what you drink with an additional glass of water. (If you drink soda, you must take 10 to 20 glasses of water to counter the amount you drink.)

• Avoid sweeteners; most are acidic in nature.

• Over-the-counter medicines are acidic. Prescription drugs are also acidic; however, if you are on prescriptions, talk with your doctor before making changes.

Remember the saying, "You can lead a horse to water, but you cannot make him drink." Improving your health is *your* choice.

Chapter 7
Miracles of Water: Amazing Secrets for Health And Wellness

In my studies, I have found that water can prevent and cure many physical ailments. Following are some of water's amazing secrets for health and wellness.

Cure Number One: Water Prevents And Cures Heartburn

Heartburn is a signal of water shortage in the upper pan of the gastrointestinal tract. It is a major thirst signal of the human body. The use of antacids or tablet medications in the treatment of this pain does not correct dehydration, and the body continues to suffer as a result of its water shortage.

Not recognizing heartburn as a sign of dehydration and treating it with antacids and pill medications will, in time, produce *inflammation of the stomach and duodenum, hiatal hernia, ulceration,* and *eventually cancers in the gastrointestinal tract, including the liver and pancreas.*

Cure Number Two: Water Prevents And Cures Arthritis

Rheumatoid joint pain, or arthritis, is a sign of water shortage in the painful joint. It can affect the young as well as the old. The use of painkillers does not cure the problem but exposes the person to further damage. Intake of water and small amounts of salt will cure this problem.

Cure Number Three: Water Prevents And Cures Back Pain

Low back pain and ankylosing arthritis of the spine are signs of water shortage in the spinal column and discs, the water cushions that support the weight of the body. These conditions should be treated with increased water intake. This, of course, is not a commercial treatment, but it is a very effective one.

Not recognizing arthritis and low back pain as signs of dehydration in the joint cavities and treating them with painkillers, manipulation, acupuncture, and/or surgery will, in time, produce osteoarthritis. When the cartilage cells in the joints have eventually all died, it will produce deformity of the spine and crippling deformities of the limbs. Furthermore, pain medications have their own life-threatening complications.

Cure Number Four: Water Prevents And Cures Angina

Heart pain (angina) is a sign of water shortage in the heart/lung axis. It should be treated with increased water intake until the patient is free of pain and independent of medications. Medical supervision is prudent. However, increased water intake is angina's cure.

Cure Number Five: Water Prevents And Cures Migraines

A migraine headache is a sign that the brain and eyes need water. This particular type of dehydration might eventually cause inflammation of the back of the eye and possibly loss of eyesight.

Cure Number Six: Water Prevents And Cures Colitis

Colitis pain is a signal of water shortage. It is associated with constipation: The large intestine constricts to squeeze the last drop of water from the excrements, thus creating the lack of water lubrication.

Not recognizing colitis pain as a sign of dehydration will cause persistent constipation. Later in life, it will cause fecal impacting: it can cause diverticulitis, hemorrhoids, polyps, and appreciably increase the possibility of developing cancers of the colon and rectum.

Cure Number Seven: Water and Salt Prevent and Cure Asthma

Asthma, which affects 12,000,000 children and kills several thousand of them every year, is a complication of dehydration in the body. It is caused by the drought management programs of the body. Free passage of air is obstructed so that water does not leave the body in the form of vapor—the winter steam. Increased water intake will prevent asthma attacks. Asthmatics need also to take more salt to break the mucus plugs in the lungs, which obstruct the free flow of air in and out of the air sacs.

Not recognizing asthma as an indicator of dehydration in the bodies of growing children will sentence many thousands of children to die every year. Not only that, but it will cause irreversible genetic damage in the remaining millions of asthmatic children.

Cure Number Eight: Water Prevents And Cures High Blood Pressure

Hypertension is a state of adaptation of the body to a generalized drought. This occurs when there is not enough water to fill all the blood vessels, which diffuse water into vital cells. As part of the process of reverse osmosis, water from the serum is filtered and injected into important cells through minute holes in their membranes. Just as a hospital technician injects I.V. "water" in a patient to keep him hydrated, so the body injects water into cells—tens of trillions of them, all at the same time! Extra pressure is needed for the "injection process." Water and some salt intake will bring blood pressure back to normal.

Not recognizing hypertension as one of the major indicators of dehydration in the human body and treating it with diuretics that further dehydrate the body will, in time, cause cholesterol blockage of the heart arteries and brain arteries. This may cause heart attacks; small and/or massive and paralyzing strokes; kidney diseases; and brain damage and neurological disorders, such as Alzheimer's Disease.

Cure Number Nine: Water Prevents and Cures Early Adult-Onset Diabetes

Adult-onset diabetes is another adaptive state to severe dehydration of the human body. When a person does not consume adequate amounts of water, in order to meet the brain's priority water needs, the release of insulin is inhibited to prevent insulin from pushing water into all body cells. In diabetes, only some cells get survival rations of water. Water and some salt will reverse adult-onset diabetes in its early stages.

Not recognizing adult-onset diabetes as a complication of dehydration may, in time, cause massive damage to the blood vessels all over the body. It could cause eventual loss of the toes, feet, and legs to gangrene. It may cause eye damage and even blindness.

Cure Number Ten: Water Lowers Blood Cholesterol

High cholesterol levels are an indicator of early drought management by the body. Cholesterol is a clay-like material that is poured in the gaps of some cell membranes to safeguard them from losing their vital water content to the osmotically more powerful blood circulating in their vicinity. Cholesterol, apart from being used to manufacture nerve cell membranes and hormones, is also used as a "shield" against water taxation of other vital cells that would normally exchange water through their cell membranes.

Cure Number Eleven: Water Cures Depression, Loss of Libido, Chronic Fatigue Syndrome, Lupus, Multiple Sclerosis, Muscular Dystrophy

These conditions are caused by prolonged chronic dehydration. They will clear up once the body becomes well and regularly hydrated. The treatment program for these conditions should also include exercising one's muscles. For more information, read the book *Your Body's Many Cries for Water.*

Chapter 8
A Call to Action

Since I started teaching on the value of water, I have received numerous reports of healing from everywhere. I constantly have a stack of letters in my office containing testimonies of those who have been helped. So far, I have only gotten one complaint. One person wrote me a note that said, "That was a nice teaching you did on water, but let's move on to something more important."

Well, besides salvation, I cannot think of anything more important in life than your health. Your health is one of your most valuable assets. You could have a million dollars; but if you weren't in good health, you would probably be willing to give it all for health. In fact, something would be wrong with you mentally if you were sick and not trying to get well. Most people would spend every cent of their money to regain their lost health, especially if their conditions were terminal.

Many people today are trying to buy their health, and doctors are still telling them there is nothing they can do. There are cases in which even a million dollars won't do the trick. But the good news is that you don't need a million dollars to walk in health. You don't even have to be rich. There aren't many things cheaper than water. As I said, God's health plan is simple, readily available, and inexpensive for everyone everywhere in the world.

We have used water for everything, but we have neglected to use it for the health of our bodies. Now we're starting to get the message. To some, it may not sound like an exciting message, but it is exciting to me when you know that something easy and practical—something that is "doable" for anyone—can protect your asset of health and save your life. This message can change your physical well-being (even if you are in good health, your health can be even better) if you will apply what you learn.

Commit to Action

I believe that we can enjoy the life of health that God has provided for us. But there is a call to action. If there is no action on your part, you are not going to live in health.

Furthermore, you have to be committed for the long haul. Yes, you will see some results quickly. However, some people will start a program of drinking more water, but it won't be a lifestyle change for them. In other words, they'll go back to drinking soda, coffee, and tea, because, deep down, they like those things better than they like being healthy or living in optimal health. That is certainly their prerogative, but I'm going to go for the gold, so to speak! I'm going to go for the long life of health and vigor and vitality that God has promised and planned for me.

I know I have a lot more water to drink, but I am going to do it! Remember, I said we must first have the desire and will to live a long, healthy life. Then it will be easier to do the things that make for a long life of health and peace.

A Word of Caution

Now if you are presently under a doctor's care, I am not telling you to go against the doctor's orders. Talk to your doctor before you make any changes with medications or treatments. You can begin right now doing the things you learned in this book *while* you are taking medications.

It takes time to regain health if you've lost it. But if you will commit yourself to drinking the right amount of water and following a healthy pattern of living, I believe you will gradually outgrow your need for medication. Your doctor will be able to see it, and he or she can advise you as to how to stop taking your medication, whether all at once or gradually.

I believe you can walk in divine health all the days of your life. And God has given you the simplest way to do it. I urge you not to ignore it. Instead, take full advantage of this wonderful resource for healing and health, and drink up! You can live well by water.

Conclusion

The simplicity of drinking water does not want to settle in man's intellect. Many will just not accept such an uncomplicated method of healing. But one with any common sense only needs to look around and see how the Creator of the earth revives and generates life into and out of dry deserts. After rains of water, dead gardens come back to life before our eyes. This entire world would dry up without water. Life will cease without water; therefore, it stands to reason that it will flourish *with* water. This is a tremendous revelation concerning water as it relates to health and healing to the physical body.

I believe that many good people, including pastors, have not seen the best years of their lives because they have died prematurely. Why? Could a lack of understanding of the importance of water be one reason? (Notice, I said *one*. Obviously, there may be other factors, but, again, I believe we may have added to them by not having this information.)

This book is from my heart, and all I want to do through it is to help people. I pray that as simple as this book might be, you will receive it in your heart and act upon it, as my congregation has done. Jesus said in John 13:17, *"If ye know these things, happy are ye if ye do them."*

The victory is in the doing. Christian or non-Christian, you should read the Scriptures. You will be blessed as you do. God wants you well.

Luke 4:17-19 in *The Amplified Bible* says:

And there was handed to Him [the roll of] the book of the prophet Isaiah. He opened (unrolled) the book and found the place where it was written, The Spirit of the Lord [is] upon Me, because He has anointed Me [the Anointed One, the Messiah] to preach the good news (the Gospel) to the poor; He has sent me to announce release to the captives and recovery of sight to the blind, to send forth as delivered those who are oppressed [who are downtrodden, bruised, crushed and broken down by calamity], to proclaim the accepted and acceptable year of the Lord [the day when salvation and the free favors of God profusely abound.

In review, recognize the fact that there are two primary causes for poor health: (1) *dehydration* and (2) *acidosis.*

Remember the fact that there are two primary factors for good health and longevity: (1) *hydration* and (2) *alkalinity.*

We really can live well by water.

Just as our prayers have been answered, I believe that your prayers will be answered. Our Father God has two principles that must be adhered to:

1. Get the knowledge (potential power).

2. Consistently do what is required of you (actual power).

You will have your own testimony, and you can be a blessing, reaching out and help others who may have no hope.

I love you and desire to hear what God has done for you. You can live well by water. Remember, water is one of God's power sources for miracles.

This simple but profound book has been written exactly as the Lord gave it to me and exactly the way it happened. Everywhere I go and share about the wonder-working miracle power of water, healing and miracles take place.

Appendix A: Testimonies

Out of the many testimonies we have received as a result of this teaching, I have selected these few to show you what can happen when you realize the importance of water to your health and put this teaching into practice.

Pastor Stan,

The whole Body of Christ needs this kind of teaching, for, though we have been freed from the power of diseases, we often succumb to the persuasion of advertising and the convenience of sodas and artificial food. As a result, we abuse the health that was paid for with His blood.

My family and I hereby pledge to take soda out of our diet and to drink more water.

G. H.

Dear Pastor Stan,

Praise the Lord in all of His glory! I had some spots on my skin that started in various hidden areas of my body. I took no concern, because they were small and hidden and appeared to be nothing but dry spots on the skin. As time progressed, the spots grew darker and larger and started to spread to noticeable areas of my body. I soon had to cover up all over so that I wouldn't have to explain to anyone what they were. I couldn't wear short sleeves or blouses with scoop necks. I went to seek advice from various dermatologists who gave me costly medications to apply to the affected areas. However, not even remotely knowing what the cause was, they simply labeled their diagnoses "a kind of psoriasis."

I started coming to Words of Life Church in July, just in time to hear you teach on the wonderful miracle of God—water. I was amazed to hear of the many diseases that a dehydrated body may contain, especially when I heard that psoriasis was included. Starting that very night, I totally stopped drinking soda and caffeine beverages. I began to take in half my body weight in water, as instructed.

In less than one month, changes started happening. My skin thoroughly cleared up, and I lost fifteen pounds by the following month. I have a never-ending appetite for water, and it is all I drink. I am totally delivered because of the knowledge taught to me through the Word of God. To God be the glory!

K.C.

Dear Pastor Stan,

Almost three years ago my daughter was born four weeks premature, and a week after bringing her home from the hospital, we discovered she had a condition known as reflux. She was strictly breastfed and thriving well; however, after every feeding she would throw up more than half of her intake. The doctors prescribed Propulsid (a drug now under investigation by the FDA and linked to heart problems) for the condition. A grandmother of another child with the same condition told me horror stories of her two-year-old granddaughter who still suffered from reflux and how distressing it was.

The doctors also told me it wasn't necessary to give her any water since I was breastfeeding her; but after six months she refused to breastfeed, so I began to give her formula. I devised a system that after each two-to-three-ounce bottle of formula she would drink three to four ounces of water (I was always a great believer in drinking a lot of water. Only after you began to teach on the healing power of water did I realize the miracle we had experienced.)

After only a month and a half of giving my daughter more than twice her body weight in water I realized the reflux stopped completely. She is one of the healthiest two-year-old children I know. She has only gone to the doctor once in a year, and that was to update her immunizations. She continues to drink a lot of water, and I thank you for bringing this important, vital message to everyone.

A.C.

Dear Pastor Stan,

What you have been teaching us about our bodies being made to operate in the alkaline range of 7.2 to 7.5 pH has really been a blessing to me, and my spirit bears witness that this is a teaching that needs to be brought to the Body of Christ.

My son Michael has been going to the dentist to have his teeth corrected by means of braces. One afternoon I heard him cry out in pain because the metal retainer in his mouth had broken and snapped into his gum. When we went to the dentist's office to have it repaired, the dentist asked me if Michael drank a lot of cola. I answered yes. The dentist then told me that cola melts the glue in the metal posts that hold the retainer and told Michael not to drink so many colas.

Thank God for pure, clean, healthy water.

B.G.

Dear Pastor Stan.

Thank God, I have been redeemed from the curse of the Law by the blood of Jesus Christ. For the longest time when I would awake in the mornings, my hands would itch so badly that I would have to scrape the palms of my hands to scratch them. My hands would become dry, and the skin would begin to peel off; hard calluses would form on the palms of my hand, and they would crack open.

Since you started teaching on our body's need for water, I have stopped drinking sodas and increased my intake of water. Now my hands no longer itch, the skin no longer peels from my hands, and the calluses are gone from the palms of my hands.

Thank you, Pastor Stan, for bringing this knowledge to the body of Christ.

G.C.

Pastor Stan,

Congratulations! I watched the last ten minutes of your sermon today on TBN. Not one pastor in a hundred will make health suggestions, but you are absolutely correct about water. You are on the right track for sure. I have been pain-free and medicine-free for eighty years doing just what you have been teaching.

Chester

Pastor Stan,

Look what the Lord has done!

I was previously diagnosed with advanced osteoporosis and two collapsed vertebrae, which led to the loss of three inches in height. Since the diagnosis, I have done everything the doctors recommended to maintain the level of bone density I have and to prevent any further fractures. But I also increased my water intake.

This week I had an appointment for a bone density test. During the test, the technician said the results didn't look right on the hip measurement, and she decided to redo that portion of the test. (I think she could not believe her eyes because of the 17 percent increase.)

The doctor said that the test results revealed that there is a 10 percent increase in bone density in my back and a 17 percent increase in bone density in my hip. There has also been a gain of one inch in height.

This disease affects men and women. It is considered the twelfth leading cause of death in the

United States. Of all bone fractures reported annually, 1.3 million are attributed to the condition (The Federal Register, November 1991).

D.M.

Dear Pastor Stan,

In November 1988, I was diagnosed with bone marrow cancer. In 1993, I was told that my condition was terminal. For twelve years, I did not receive any type of chemotherapy.

Doctors do not understand how I can live so long with terminal cancer. Most patients with this type of cancer normally live three to six years, which was the life expectancy they gave me. They cannot understand why I do not have holes in my bones by now.

On August 4, 2000, I was taken to Parkway Medical Center's emergency room with the following conditions:

1. Unconsciousness

2. Respiratory failure

3. Fever, temperature 104.8° Fahrenheit

4. Heartbeat: 222 beats per minute

5. Blood pressure 200/130

6. Pneumonia

7. Bacterial meningitis (inflammation of the spinal cord and the lining of the brain)

8. Blood was sludge

9. Hemorrhaging from the nose

10. Multiple melanomas (bone cancer)

11. Zero immune system (due to bone cancer)

That same week, it was reported on television that two healthy young men, ages seventeen and twenty-one, died of meningitis. The doctors said that if I had arrived at the hospital two hours later I would have been dead upon arrival. Bacterial meningitis is the worst kind of meningitis a person can contract.

I was in ICU for ten days, unconscious and on a ventilator. The doctors did not think I was going to live. The primary-care physician informed my family that I might need a tracheotomy and a feeding tube placed in my intestines and to be kept alive by machines.

My family was informed that I might be a "vegetable" if and when I did wake up. The doctors said that most patients who have been unconscious and on the ventilator for the length of time I was, usually wake up brain-dead.

I had a blood specialist, pulmonary specialist, kidney specialist, infectious disease specialist, neurologist, primary care physician, and the Great Physician working on my case!

While I was unconscious, I had numerous visitation with Abraham and others, along with thousands of angels. What a trip! By the grace of God, on the eleventh day, I woke up breathing on my own with all my faculties and a sound mind.

Today, nine weeks later, I stand in God's amazing grace, giving Him all the praise and all the glory. I am healed, walking in divine health. I also drink a gallon and a half of water per day, thanks to your teaching.

James 1:2-4 in *The New Living Translation* says, "Dear brothers and sisters, whenever trouble comes your way, let it be an opportunity for joy. For when your faith is tested, your endurance has a chance to grow. So let it grow, for when your endurance is fully developed, you will be strong in character and ready for anything."

I can truly say, according to Psalm 66:12 that God has brought me out into a wealthy place. Thank you, Pastor Stan, for all your teaching on the Blood and water and how to pray. I thank Words of Life Fellowship Church for their corporate prayers, and I thank my family and friends for their individual prayers. The devil has been defeated, retreated, and beaten.

We love and thank God for what He is doing in your life and in Words of Life Church. We are grateful for you and your beautiful family.

To God be the glory. We stand in His amazing grace,

R.P.

Dear Pastor Stan,

Please don't stop teaching on water! It has saved my life! Your teaching on water has helped me get off medication I have been taking for years. Doctors told me I would never be able to get off this medication and live. I was taking the largest dose possible of this medication, five times a day. The dose was so large, it shocked pharmacists when they filled the prescription. If I missed even one dose, I was in trouble. Because I took so much of this medication, it was making me very ill with side-effects. I was sick if I took the medication, and I was sick without it.

I had been standing on God's Word for my deliverance from this medication and illness, candida yeast, for three years. God told me to do some things in the natural and the Spirit realm, which I did. I would get some victory; however, I would end up back where I started. Something was missing.

Your teaching on water was the missing link in my recovery.

I already drank eight glasses of water a day, so I thought I was doing all right with my water intake. However, the Sunday you said we needed a "hin," as the Bible says [Ezekiel 4:11], or a gallon a day, something went off in my spirit, and I knew that was it!

I began immediately to drink a gallon or more a day. At every symptom, I drank at least sixteen ounces of water. I noticed I needed less and less medication. When a symptom came, the water stopped it faster than the medication did.

Candida yeast thrives in an acid environment. With the water, I was literally putting out the fire they were living in! They had to die.

By now I would have taken the medication close to 300 times. I have only taken it seven or eight times, and that was early on when I first started tapering off of it. I have not had to take any in over a month, and my doctor is thrilled. I am praising God for your teaching. Don't stop!

I love you.

J.F.

Dear Pastor Stan,

I just want to thank you for your boldness in teaching on the subject of water, which is not a popular subject in churches and ministries today. I believe wholeheartedly that God has selected you to present this message to the Body of Christ, so that God's children can be kept out of clinics, doctor's offices, and hospitals.

Pastor Stan, I have been a medical professional for nineteen years and have seen diseases and death of all types. I have seen so many people die of dehydration, cancer, liver disease, and HIV, just to name a few. When they come into the hospital dying, we try to resuscitate them with intravenous fluids (water), but sometimes it is too late.

These days, the physicians have so many patients due to "managed care" that they hardly have time to see them. Lots of unnecessary tests and medications are prescribed for these patients who have no insight or knowledge of their illness.

This is why I believe that water is God's method of keeping us healthy and out of the hands of those physicians and away from hospital beds. I was always a water drinker; however, since you started this teaching, I have increased my volume to two to three liters per day. So far, several miracles have taken place. They are as follows:

- I sleep better.

- I wake up easier.
- I feel stronger.
- My acne is clearing up.
- Menstrual cramps are gone.
- My system is more regular.

Pastor, I have also shared your tapes with a friend in Texas who also is a Christian and loves God. The first time I told her about the teaching of water, she could not stop shouting and praising the Lord on the phone. She said, "This word bears witness with my spirit. God has been telling me to hydrate myself to better health."

She said, "This is an anointed word straight from God's throne room. Drinking that water is going to heal people in that church with congestive heart failure, colon cancer, asthma, and kidney disease. She encouraged me to stay on the Word and to flow with that anointed teaching so that I can remain healthy. I am also encouraging the Words of Life body to stay with it: It works!

Thank you, Pastor Stan, for raising the standard to a healthy body, better living, and longer life. It is not you; it is the Holy Spirit, and you are God's vessel. God bless you. I love you.

E.F.

Appendix B: Scriptures

Out of more than 700 scriptures about this topic, I have selected these few to show you the importance of this message, both spiritually and physically. I have divided the scriptures into to sections: "Water" and "Salt." In the latter section, I have inserted a few thoughts on the spiritual relevance of salt.

As you look at God's thoughts about this subject, I want you to remember John 13:17 once again: *"If ye know these things, happy are ye if ye do them."*

Water

In the beginning God created the heaven and the earth. And the earth was without form, and void; and darkness was upon the face of the deep. And the Spirit of God moved upon the face of the waters.

Genesis 1:1,2

And God said, Let the waters under the heaven be gathered together unto one place, and let the dry land appear: and it was so. And God called the dry land Earth; and the gathering together of the waters called he Seas: and God saw that it was good.

Genesis 1:9,10

But there went up a mist from the earth, and watered the whole face of the ground. And the Lord God formed man of the dust of the ground, and breathed into his nostrils the breath of life; and man became a living soul.

Genesis 2:6,7

And the Lord said, My spirit shall not always strive with man, for that he also is flesh: yet his days shall be an hundred and twenty years.

Genesis 6:3

So Moses brought Israel from the Red sea, and they went out into the wilderness of Shur; and they went three days in the wilderness, and found no water. And when they came to Marah, they could not drink of the waters of Marah, for they were bitter [acidic]: therefore the name of it was called Marah. And the people murmured against Moses, saying, What shall we drink? And he cried unto the Lord; and the Lord shewed him a tree, which when he had cast into the waters, the waters were made sweet [alkaline]: there he made for them a statute and an ordinance, and there he proved them, and said, If thou wilt diligently hearken to the voice of the Lord thy God, and wilt do that which is right in his sight, and wilt give ear to his commandments, and keep all his statutes, I will put none of these diseases upon thee, which I have brought upon the Egyptians: for I am the Lord that healeth thee. And they came to Elim, where were twelve wells of water, and threescore and ten palm trees: and they encamped there by the waters.

Exodus 15:22-27

And ye shall serve the Lord your God,
and he shall bless thy bread, and thy
water; and I will take sickness away
from the midst of thee.

Exodus 23:25

For the Lord thy God bringeth thee into
a good land, a land of brooks of water,
of fountains and depths that spring out
of valleys and hills.

Deuteronomy 8:7

And when he came unto Lehi, the
Philistines shouted against him: and
the Spirit of the Lord came mightily
upon him, and the cords that were upon
his arms became as flax that was burnt
with fire, and his bands loosed from off
his hands. And he found a new jawbone
of an ass, and put forth his hand, and
took it, and slew a thousand men there-
with. And Samson said, With the jawbone of an ass, heaps upon heaps, with
the jaw of an ass have I slain a thousand men. And it came to pass, when he
had made an end of speaking, that he

cast away the jawbone out of his hand, and called that place Ramathlehi. And he was sore athirst, and called on the Lord, and said, Thou hast given this great deliverance into the hand of thy servant: and now shall I die for thirst, and fall into the hand of the uncircumcised? But God clave an hollow place that was in the jaw, and there came water thereout; and when he had drunk, his spirit came again, and he revived: wherefore he called the name thereof Enhakkore, which is in Lehi unto this day.

Judges 15:14-19

And the men of the city said unto Elisha, Behold, I pray thee, the situation of this city is pleasant, as my lord seeth: but the water is naught [bitter], and the ground barren. And he said, Bring me a new cruse, and put salt therein. And they brought it to him. And he went forth unto the spring of the waters, and cast the salt in there, and said, Thus saith the Lord, I have

healed these waters; there shall not be
from thence any more death or barren
land. So the waters were healed unto
this day, according to the saying of
Elisha which he spake.

2 Kings 2:19-22

Now Naaman, captain of the host of the
king of Syria, was a great man with his
master, and honourable, because by
him the Lord had given deliverance
unto Syria: he was also a mighty man in
valour, but he was a leper.... So Naaman
came with his horses and with his char-
iot, and stood at the door of the house
of Elisha. And Elisha sent a messenger
unto him, saying, Go and wash in
Jordan seven times, and thy flesh shall
come again to thee, and thou shalt be
clean.... Then went he down, and
dipped himself seven times in Jordan,
according to the saying of the man of
God: and his flesh came again like unto
the flesh of a little child, and he was
clean.

2 Kings 5:1,9,10,14

Thou visitest the earth, and waterest it: thou greatly enrichest it with the river of God, which is full of water: thou pre-parest them corn, when thou hast so provided for it. Thou waterest the ridges thereof abundantly: thou settlest the furrows thereof: thou makest it soft with showers: thou blessest the spring-ing thereof. Thou crownest the year with thy goodness; and thy paths drop fatness. They drop upon the pastures of the wilderness: and the little hills rejoice on every side. The pastures are clothed with flocks; the valleys also are covered over with corn; they shout for joy, they also sing.

                              Psalm 65:9-13

Therefore my people are gone into cap-tivity, because they have no knowledge: and their honourable men are fam-ished, and their multitude dried up with thirst.... Woe unto them that are mighty to drink wine, and men of strength to mingle strong drink.... Therefore as the fire devoureth the stubble, and the flame consumeth the chaff, so their root shall be as rottenness, and their blossom shall go up as dust: because they have cast away the law of the Lord of hosts, and despised the word of the Holy One of Israel.

Isaiah 5:13,22,24

Behold, God is my salvation; I will trust, and not be afraid: for the Lord Jehovah is my strength and my song; he also is become my salvation. Therefore with joy shall ye draw water out of the wells of salvation.

Isaiah 12:2-3

For as the rain cometh down, and the snow from heaven, and returneth not thither, but watereth the earth, and maketh it bring forth and bud, that it may give seed to the sower, and bread to the eater: So shall my word be that goeth forth out of my mouth: it shall not return unto me void, but it shall accomplish that which I please, and it shall prosper in the thing whereto I sent it.

                                                Isaiah 55:10,11

And the Lord shall guide thee continually, and satisfy thy soul in drought, and make fat thy bones: and thou shalt be like a watered garden, and like a spring of water, whose waters fail not.

                                                Isaiah 58:11

Thou shalt drink also water by measure, the sixth part of an hin: from time to time shalt thou drink.... Moreover he said unto me, Son of man, behold, I will break the staff of bread in Jerusalem: and they shall eat bread by weight, and with care; and they shall drink water by measure, and with astonishment.

                                                Ezekiel 4:11,16

My people are destroyed for lack of knowledge: because thou hast rejected knowledge, I will also reject thee, that thou shalt be no priest to me: seeing

thou hast forgotten the law of thy God,
I will also forget thy children.

Hosea 4:6

And it came to pass in those days, that
Jesus came from Nazareth of Galilee,
and was baptized of John in [the waters
of] Jordan. And straightway coming up
out of the water, he saw the heavens
opened, and the Spirit like a dove
descending upon him: and there came a
voice from heaven, saying, Thou art my
beloved Son, in whom I am well
pleased.

Mark 1:9-11

There was a man of the Pharisees,
named Nicodemus, a ruler of the Jews:
the same came to Jesus by night, and
said unto him, Rabbi, we know that
thou art a teacher come from God: for
no man can do these miracles that thou
doest, except God be with him. Jesus
answered and said unto him, Verily,
verily, I say unto thee, Except a man be
born again, he cannot see the kingdom

of God. Nicodemus saith unto him, How can a man be born when he is old? can he enter the second time into his mother's womb, and be born? Jesus answered, Verily, verily, I say unto thee, Except a man be born of water and of the Spirit, he cannot enter into the kingdom of God.

John 3:1-5

Jesus answered and said unto her, Whosoever drinketh of this water shall thirst again: but whosoever drinketh of the water that I shall give him shall never thirst; but the water that I shall give him shall be in him a well of water springing up into everlasting life.

John 4:13-14

Now there is at Jerusalem by the sheep market a pool, which is called in the Hebrew tongue Bethesda, having five porches. In these lay a great multitude of impotent folk, of blind, halt, withered, waiting for the moving of the water. For an angel went down at a certain season into the pool, and troubled the water: whosoever then first after the troubling of the water stepped in was made whole of whatsoever disease he had.

John 5:2-4

And as Jesus passed by, he saw a man which was blind from his birth. And his disciples asked him, saying, Master, who did sin, this man, or his parents, that he was born blind? Jesus answered, Neither hath this man sinned, nor his parents: but that the works of God should be made manifest in him. I must work the works of him that sent me, while it is day: the night cometh, when no man can work. As long as I am in the world, I am the light of the world. When he had thus spoken, he spat on the ground, and made clay of the spittle, and he anointed the eyes of the blind man with the clay, and said unto him, Go, wash in the pool of Siloam, (which is by interpretation,

Sent.) He went his way therefore, and washed, and came seeing.

John 9:1-7

But God hath chosen the foolish things of the world to confound the wise; and God hath chosen the weak things of the world to confound the things which are mighty; and base things of the world, and things which are despised, hath God chosen, yea, and things which are not, to bring to nought things that are: that no flesh should glory in his presence. But of him are ye in Christ Jesus, who of God is made unto us wisdom, and righteousness, and sanctification, and redemption: that, according as it is written, He that glorieth, let him glory in the Lord.

1 Corinthians 1:27-31

Which sometime were disobedient, when once the longsuffering of God waited in the days of Noah, while the ark was a preparing, wherein few, that is, eight souls were saved by water.

1 Peter 3:20

This is he that came by water and
blood, even Jesus Christ; not by water
only, but by water and blood. And it is
the Spirit that beareth witness, because
the Spirit is truth. For there are three
that bear record in heaven, the Father,
the Word, and the Holy Ghost: and
these three are one. And there are three
that bear witness in earth, the Spirit,
and the water, and the blood: and these
three agree in one.

                              1 John 5:6-8

Beloved, I wish above all things that
thou mayest prosper and be in health,
even as thy soul prospereth.

                              3 John 2

Salt

• In the Old Testament, newborn babies were
sprinkled with salt to make their flesh firmer.

Covenant of Salt

• Salt was a symbol of friendship.

• Salt was a symbol of preservation.

And every oblation of thy meat offering shalt thou season with salt; neither shalt thou suffer the salt of the covenant of thy God to be lacking from thy meat offering: with all thine offerings thou shalt offer salt.
Leviticus 2:13

• Salt was a symbol of duration and perpetuity.

All the heave offerings of the holy things, which the children of Israel offer unto the Lord, have I given thee, and thy sons and thy daughters with thee, by a statute for ever: it is a covenant of salt for ever before the Lord unto thee and to thy seed with thee.
Numbers 18:19

• Salt was a symbol of a perpetual covenant between God and Israel, which He renews daily and confirms.

Ought ye not to know that the Lord God of Israel gave the kingdom over Israel to David for ever, even to him and to his sons by a covenant of salt?

2 Chronicles 13:5

For every one shall be salted with fire, and every sacrifice shall be salted with salt. Salt is good [beneficial]**: but if the salt have lost his saltness, wherewith will ye season** [or restore] **it? Have salt in yourselves, and have peace** [harmony] **one with another.**

Mark 9:49,50